THE LAST JEDI

THE QUEST FOR LUKE SKYWALKER

ACT 1

Adapted by Michael Kogge

studio
INTERNATIONAL

The destruction of Starkiller Base has only served to strengthen the First Order's resolve. Supreme Leader Snoke orders its mighty military to seize control of the galaxy. Only the Resistance stands in its way.

General Leia Organa and her new allies, Rey, Finn, and Poe, cling to the hope that Jedi Master Luke Skywalker will come to help them. But with every passing minute, their hope is dwindling . . .

1

DISK 1

Finn wakes with a jolt. He finds himself in the medical bay of a Resistance star cruiser. Instead of clothes, he's wearing a special body suit that helps heal his wounds.

His last memory is dueling Kylo Ren, the most notorious villain of the First Order, while trying to rescue his friend, Rey.

The cruiser suddenly shakes and Resistance soldiers rush by him in the hallway. A viewport shows First Order warships attacking the Resistance fleet!

Finn looks everywhere for Rey, but he can't find her. He does find his other friend, Poe Dameron. The pilot tells Finn that the First Order tracked the Resistance down after they destroyed Starkiller Base. Poe led X-wing, A-wing, and bomber squadrons to repel the First Order attackers. The bombers knocked out a massive First Order warship and helped the Resistance fleet escape into hyperspace.

Poe notices that Finn's body suit is leaking and gives him fresh clothes. As for Rey, Poe mentions she's on an important mission for General Organa.

Rey, Chewbacca the Wookiee, and R2-D2 fly the *Millennium Falcon* to the planet Ahch-To. A map indicated Jedi Master Luke Skywalker might be hiding on this forgotten world, so the General sent Rey there to persuade Luke to join the Resistance and help turn the tide of the war.

Water covers much of Ahch-To. Rey lands the *Falcon* on a rocky island in the ocean. It seems empty at first, but flocks of birdlike porgs and beings called the Caretakers live there. The Caretakers look after the secrets of the island.

1

DISK 2

Rey finds Luke Skywalker standing at the edge of a cliff. He is dressed in dirty robes and has a beard. She approaches, removing his lightsaber from her bag. She found it in Maz Kanata's castle on Takodana, and wants to return it to Luke.

Luke won't take the lightsaber, so Rey places it in his hand. After looking at it, he refuses to take the lightsaber and throws it over the cliff.

Rey is baffled. This man is not the wise Jedi Master she expected!

Rey trails Luke into a village of stone huts. He enters the largest building. She tries to go in after him, but Luke slams the door in her face. No matter how hard she knocks, Luke refuses to answer. Frustrated, she walks away.

Rey returns to the cliff, and notices something on a patch of grass below and climbs down. She finds Luke's lightsaber there. A bunch of porgs scatter as she reaches to retrieve it.

She then sees something strange in a tide pool below her. Luke's old X-wing starfighter lays underwater near the seashore. Rey realizes Luke allowed it to sink because he never intends to leave Ahch-To.

3

Chewbacca becomes furious when he learns that Luke won't talk to Rey. He goes to Luke's hut and yanks off the door!

Luke is surprised to see his old friend. He asks where Han Solo is. Rey comes into the hut behind Chewie. Her silence and the Wookiee's moan tells him what he feared.

Han Solo is dead.

Luke sits with Chewbacca and Rey in the village outside his hut, listening to Rey. She reveals that Kylo Ren killed Han Solo. The news hurts Luke. She begs that he come back with her in the *Falcon*. The Resistance needs him to stop the First Order from conquering the galaxy.

Luke thinks about it, and then says simply, "No." He retreats into his hut.

Rey is distressed, but she isn't ready to give up.